CW00409498

The Christmas Story

by Mark Golding
Arranged and edited by Alison Hedger

The traditional Biblical Nativity Story retold in narration and
8 new songs for performance by children.

Opportunities for recorder and percussion and some two-part singing.
All second parts are optional. To be sung as a concert
piece or as a musical framework for a Nativity Play.

Duration approx. 25 mins.

For children 5 to 12 years
Key Stage 1 + and 2

Suitable for mixed ages and abilities.

TEACHER'S BOOK
Complete with piano accompaniment, chord symbols, vocal lines,
recorder and percussion parts.

SONGS

1. The Christmas Story *All + recorder and percussion*
2. Ave Maria *All + solo Mary, two-part singing, and recorder*
3. Rocky Road *All + glockenspiel and percussion*
4. Walking, Walking *All + percussion*
5. Lullaby *All + solo Mary and Joseph*
6. Gloria *All + two-part recorder*
7. Travelling On *All + two-part singing*
8. Now Is The Time To Sing *All*
Finale Repeat of Song 1.

Alison Hedger

The songs are colourful, easy to learn and have an up-to-date feeling which makes them instantly
appealing to children, teachers, parents and friends. Ideal for those with little time to spend on rehearsals.

The pupil's book GA 10967 contains the narrative and song words. A matching tape of the music for rehearsals and
performances is also available, Order No GA 10972. Side A with vocals included. Side B with vocals omitted.

© Copyright 1994 Golden Apple Productions
A division of Chester Music Limited
8/9 Frith Street, London W1V 5TZ

Order No. GA 10953 ISBN 0-7119-4323-0

1 THE CHRISTMAS STORY

All + recorder and percussion
Free use of percussion instruments:
guiro, tambourine, drum set, etc.

Cue 1: The time of His coming is called Christmas.
Cue 2: …again, year after year.

C D E F G A C' D' F'

Forward to ✱ on opposite page after verse 3, to complete song

It's a sto-ry of won - der, a sto-ry of good - ness, a
It's a sto-ry of hard - ship when Ma-ry and Jo - seph

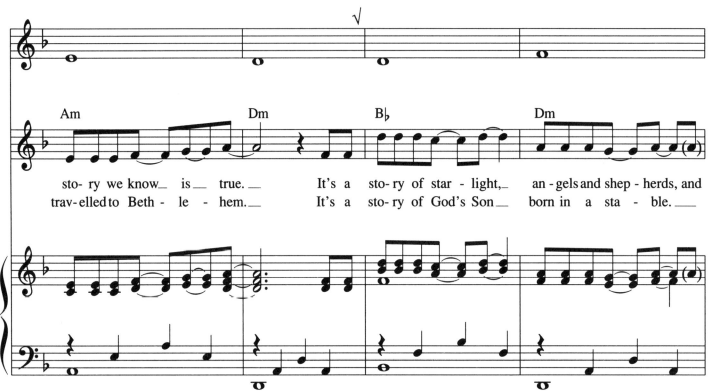

sto- ry we know__ is__ true. __ It's a sto-ry of star - light,__ an - gels and shep - herds, and
trav-elled to Beth - le - hem.__ It's a sto-ry of God's Son__ born in a sta - ble.__

2 AVE MARIA

All + solo Mary, two-part singing and recorder.
Recorder part as solo before verse 1 and as a countermelody to verse 3.
Cue: ...and that He would be God's own Son.

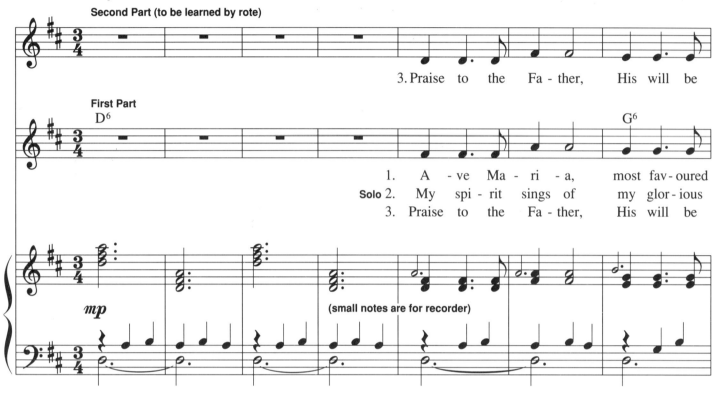

Second Part (to be learned by rote)

3. Praise to the Fa - ther, His will be

First Part

1. A - ve Ma - ri - a, most fav - oured
Solo 2. My spi - rit sings of my glor - ious
3. Praise to the Fa - ther, His will be

(small notes are for recorder)

done. God in his wis - dom send - ing His Son. Je - sus the
one. You have been cho - sen to bear God's Son. He will be
Lord. I am His ser - vant, I hear His word. Let all this
done. God in His wis - dom send - ing His Son. Je - sus the

Sav - iour, rul - er di - vine. His reign will last till the end of all

F#m/B Bm   F#m   G   Em⁷   D⁶   A⁷ᵒᵘˢ⁴ A⁷

Je - sus, rul - er di - vine. His reign will last till the end of all
hap - pen just as you say. I will give thanks for God's won - der - ful
Sav - iour, rul - er di - vine. His reign will last till the end of all

To finish

time. _____

D⁶   D

time. _____
way. _____
time. _____

p

pp

8ᵛᵇ

Recorder notes

D A B C#' D' E' F#'

7

3 ROCKY ROAD

All + glockenspiel and percussion
Add non-pitched percussion as desired.
Cue: ...almost due to be born.

3. Miles and miles have passed to-day, man-y more lie a-head. Pac-ing to the rhy-thm of a

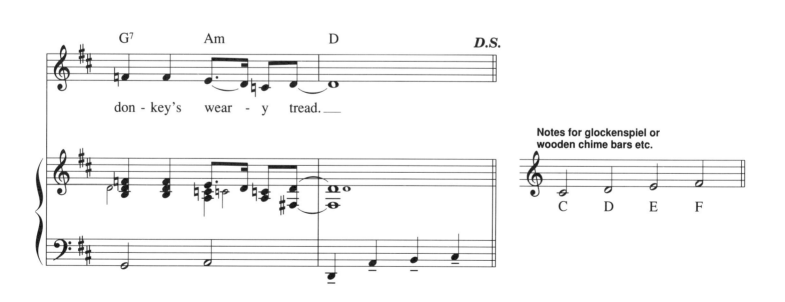

don - key's wear - y tread.

Notes for glockenspiel or wooden chime bars etc.

C D E F

4 WALKING, WALKING

All + percussion
Woodblock and claves at walking pace.

Cue: ...could find nowhere to stay.

Rhythmically ♩ = 95

Lyrics:

1.
2. Walk - ing, walk - ing, { search - ing eve - ry - where. No - one seems to have a room to
   far a - way from home. Feel - ing ve - ry lost and all a -
3. search - ing through the town. Day is done, the sun is go - ing

spare. }
- lone. } Keep on walk - ing, { try - ing eve - ry inn.
down. } wear - y as can be.
ask - ing once a - gain

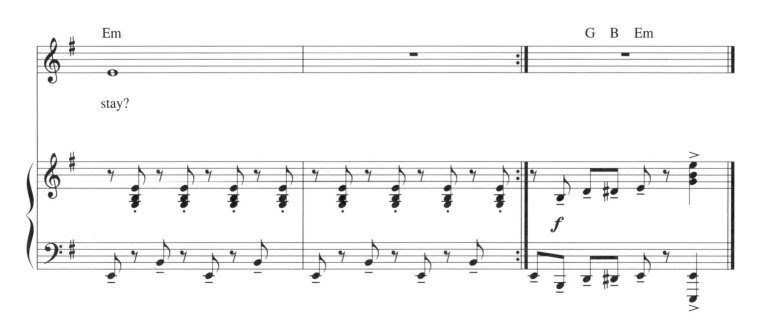

5 LULLABY

All + solo Mary and Joseph
Cue: ...made a bed for the baby.

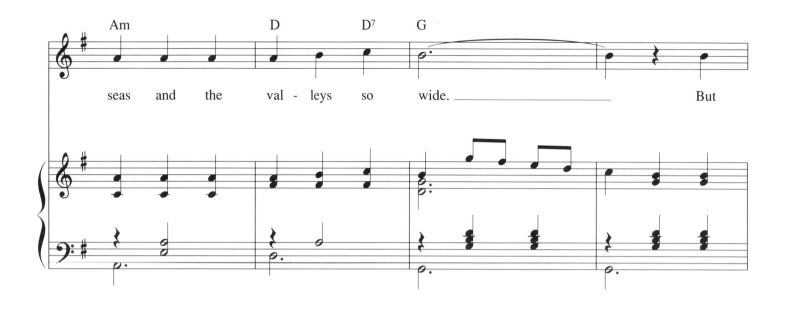

seas and the val - leys so wide. _____ But

great - est of all is this mir - a - cle boy. A

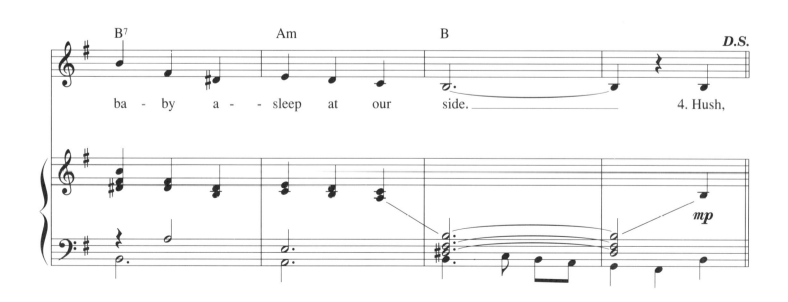

ba - by a - sleep at our side. _____ 4. Hush,

D.S.

14

6 GLORIA

All + two-part recorder
Cue: "…His peace to everyone."

birth.
bring.

Peace to all peo-ple on earth.
Wel-come the birth of your King.

3. You __ will find __ Him

ve - ry close by, a - sleep in a man-ger He lies.

4. Glo - ry to God __ in the

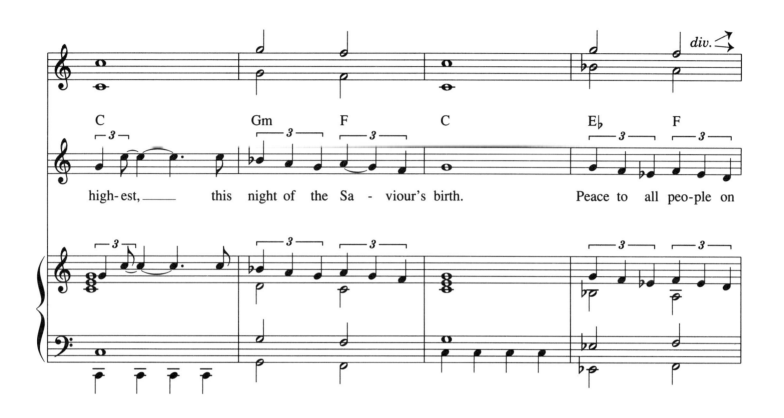

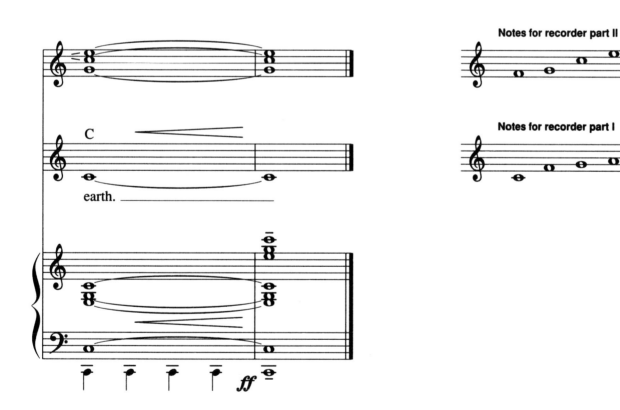

Notes for recorder part II

Notes for recorder part I

7 TRAVELLING ON

All + two-part singing
Cue: …travelled to Bethlehem.

8 NOW IS THE TIME TO SING

All
Cue: …gifts of gold, frankincense and myrrh.

1. Now, now is the time to sing. Sing, sing of the joy that is Christ - mas time.
2. Peace, peace has come to our world. Joy, fil - ling our hearts at this Christ - mas time.
3. Sing, sing Him a song of peace. Give, give Him your love at this Christ - mas time.

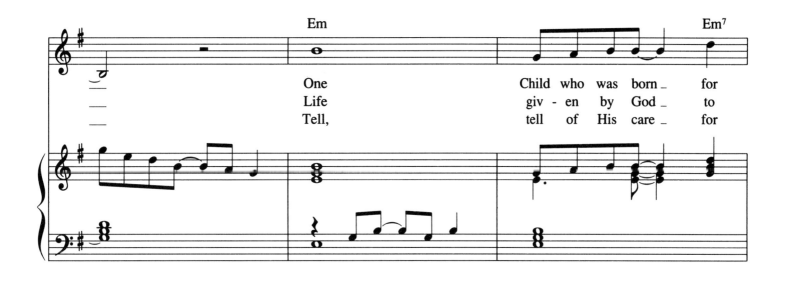

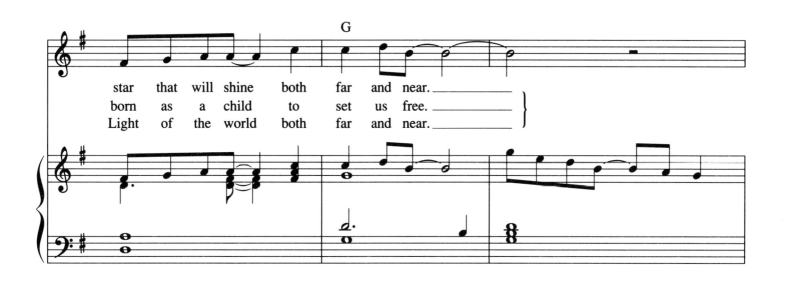

Ring, ring out the bells across the world,

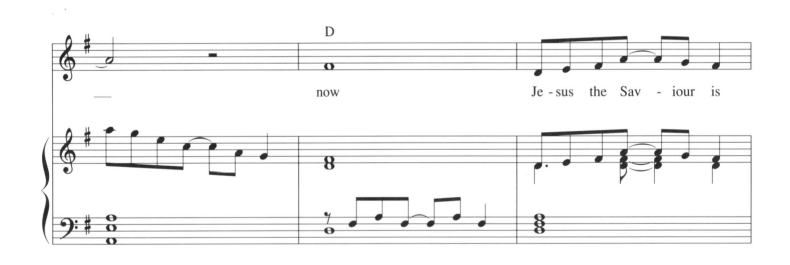

now Je - sus the Sav - iour is

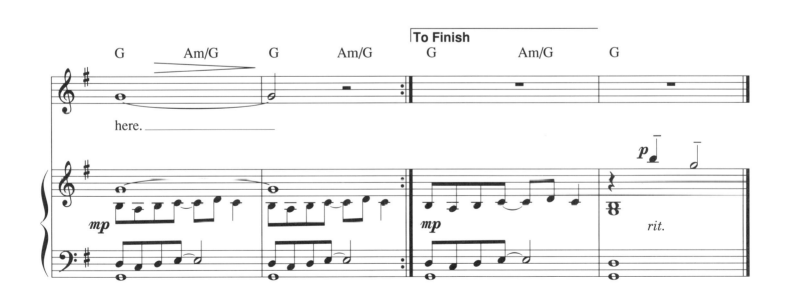

here.

1 THE CHRISTMAS STORY

Recorder

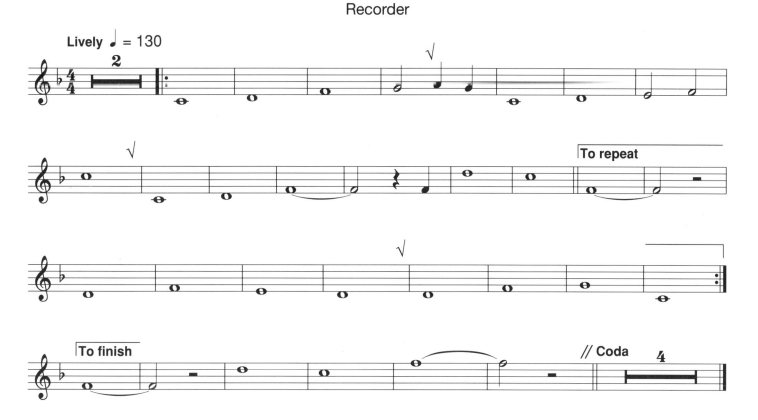

2 AVE MARIA

Recorder
Solo before verse 1 and as a countermelody to verse 3.

3 ROCKY ROAD

Glockenspiel

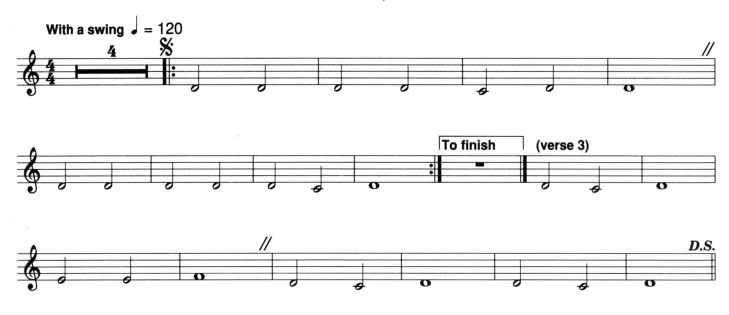

6 GLORIA

Two-part recorder